Twins Are Swell

By Liza Charlesworth

ISBN: 978-1-339-02671-8

Art Director: Tannaz Fassihi; Designer: Tanya Chernyak
Photos © Getty Images and Shutterstock.com.
Copyright © Liza Charlesworth. All rights reserved. Published by Scholastic Inc.

3 4 5 6 7 8 9 10   68   32 31 30 29 28 27 26 25 24

Printed in Jiaxing, China. First printing, August 2023.

SCHOLASTIC

It is a set of kid twins.
Twins are swell!

Frog twins hop in a pond.
Swim, swim!

Cat twins lap up milk.
Swig, swig!

Bug twins sit on a bud.
Buzz, buzz!

Cub twins run and romp.
Grrrr, Grrrr!

Snake twins rest on a twig.
Twist, twist!

Kid twins get dog twins.
Twins are swell!